LET YOUR PRACTICE BE A CELEBRATION OF LIFE.

—SEIDO LEE DeBARROS

SUN SALUTATIONS CAN ENERGIZE AND WARM YOU, EVEN ON THE DARKEST, COLDEST WINTER DAY.

—CAROL KRUCOFF

REMEMBER,
IT DOESN'T MATTER
HOW DEEP INTO A
POSTURE YOU GO—
WHAT DOES MATTER IS
WHO YOU
ARE WHEN YOU GET THERE.
–MAX STROM

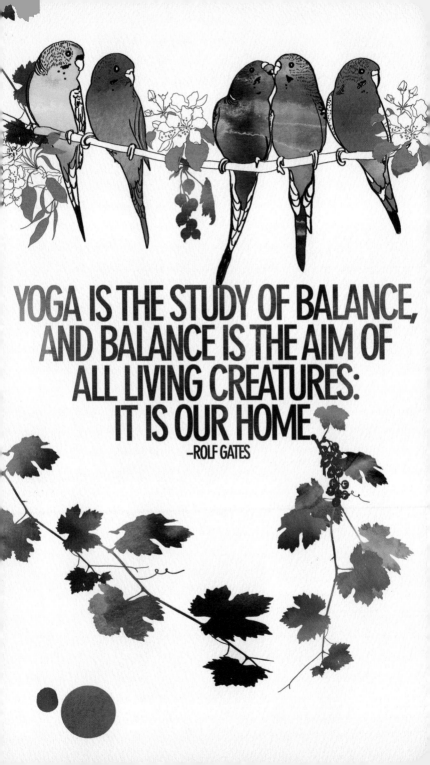

YOGA IS THE STUDY OF BALANCE, AND BALANCE IS THE AIM OF ALL LIVING CREATURES: IT IS OUR HOME.
—ROLF GATES

YOUR VISION WILL
BECOME CLEAR ONLY WHEN YOU
LOOK INTO YOUR HEART...
WHO LOOKS OUTSIDE,
DREAMS.
WHO LOOKS INSIDE,
AWAKENS.
–CARL JUNG

WITHOUT THE BODY, THE WISDOM OF THE LARGER SELF CANNOT BE KNOWN.

-JOHN CONGER

I HAVE NOT ENCOUNTERED
ANOTHER TEMPLE
AS BLISSFUL AS MY OWN BODY.
–SAHARA

YOGA IS A LIGHT, WHICH ONCE LIT, WILL NEVER DIM. THE BETTER YOUR PRACTICE, THE BRIGHTER THE FLAME.

—B.K.S. IYENGAR